The Little Dragon

Written by Sheri Fink

Illustrations by Lynx Studios

Books by Sheri Fink:

The Little Rose
The Little Gnome
The Little Firefly
Exploring the Garden with the Little Rose
The Little Seahorse
Counting Sea Life with the Little Seahorse
The Little Unicorn
World of Whimsy with the Little Unicorn

THE LITTLE DRAGON
By Sheri Fink

Library of Congress Control Number: 2019903096
ISBN: 978-1-949213-03-4

Printed in China
FIRST EDITION

This book is dedicated with love
to my father, David.
Thank you for dancing with me.

In a whimsical land beyond the sparkling sea lived a happy-go-lucky Little Dragon. He spent his days in the meadow watching the carefree clouds drift by.

At night, he loved sleeping in his comfy cave and dreaming under the starry sky.

The Little Dragon treasured time on his own exploring, thinking, and most of all, dancing. One day, while he was in the middle of a particularly expressive dance among the daisies, he was startled to discover that he wasn't alone.

Someone was watching and giggling while hiding behind a tree at the edge of the meadow. The Little Dragon felt scared and embarrassed. He immediately stopped and froze in place wondering who or what was watching him and how long they'd been there.

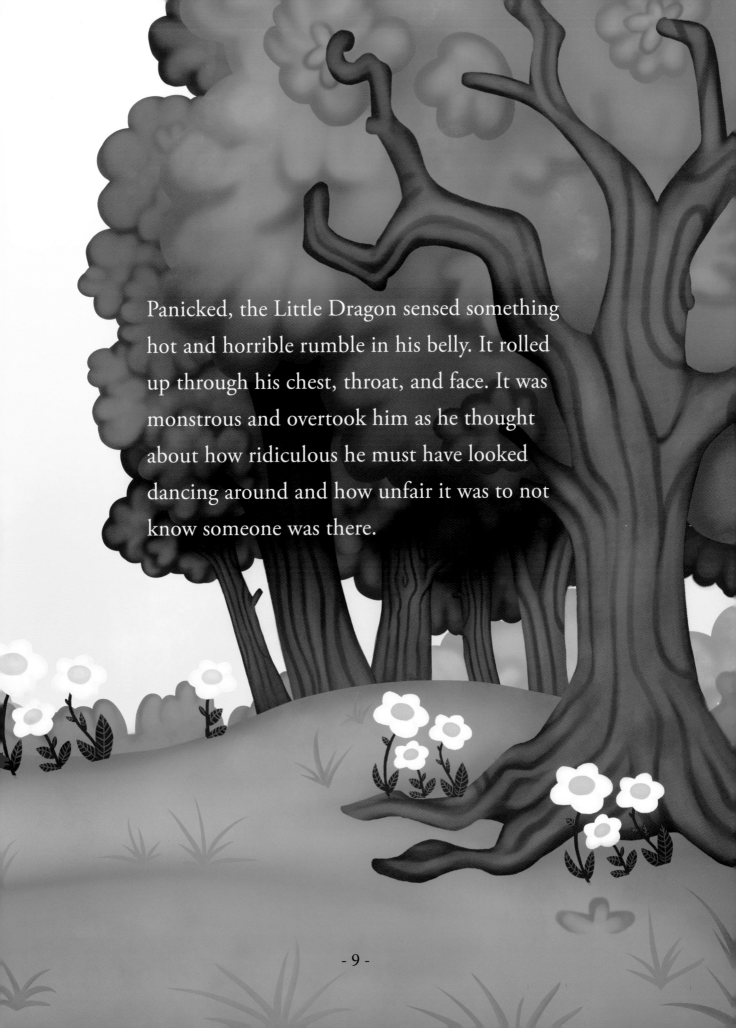

Panicked, the Little Dragon sensed something hot and horrible rumble in his belly. It rolled up through his chest, throat, and face. It was monstrous and overtook him as he thought about how ridiculous he must have looked dancing around and how unfair it was to not know someone was there.

His chest and face inflamed. It felt like a giant balloon was about to explode from inside. The heat burned his eyes and nose. He opened his mouth to gasp for air and a big curl of fire blazed out along with a mighty roar!

The giggling stopped. Through the eerie silence he could hear his heart pounding. The Little Dragon had never experienced this sensation before. What had just happened? He looked up and saw that he had scorched the side of a beautiful tree. He loved the flower-filled meadow. What if his angry burst of fire had burned it all away?

Feeling shocked and ashamed, the Little Dragon ran home and curled up in his cave. He flopped down onto his cozy cushion and wrapped his long, scaly tail around himself, covering his face.

What should I do? he wondered. *Should I hide in this cave forever? Maybe I could move to a land far away where no one will laugh at me? But, what if I leave and someone ruins my special meadow?*

He couldn't stand the thought of something happening to his happy place. Feeling the need to protect it, he devised a plan.

He asked the birds if they'd seen anyone in the area. They all told him the same thing—that it was a dragon. He didn't know exactly what that was, but he was going to make sure that his meadow was kept safe.

That night, the Little Dragon stayed up late gathering broken tree branches from the forest and creating signs. He painstakingly posted them the next morning. From now on, anyone who happened to find his meadow would know that there were "No dragons allowed."

He felt very satisfied knowing that his meadow was secure. Before bed, the Little Dragon celebrated with a bubble bath and imagined blowing his troubles into the bubbles and watching them float away.

He could hardly wait to get to the meadow the next morning. The sun was shining so brightly that the flowers looked as if they were glowing. The Little Dragon sashayed through the snapdragons and twirled amongst the tulips until he heard it… Giggling! It seemed to be coming from behind the same tree as before.

Oh no! thought the Little Dragon. Feeling the same growling sensation start inside his stomach, he decided to take a deep breath. After all, the signs clearly said, "No dragons allowed." Then he had a new worry. *What if dragons can't read and barge into my meadow?*

"Hey!" he heard a voice
calling to him from the
meadow's edge.
He saw a shadowed
figure peek her head out
from behind the tree.

The girl giggled as she sauntered toward him, revealing
her long snout, little wings, and scaly back and tail.

"Can't you see that no dragons are allowed in this meadow?" she asked with a smile. The Little Dragon regained his composure and responded, "That's right. So, go away!"

NO DRAGONS ALLOWED

"But you're a dragon, too," she whispered to him. The Little Dragon slowly stepped toward her to get a better look. He stared at her features and then examined his own in disbelief. He felt his cheeks flush. She was right, they did look very similar.

Suddenly he felt silly for putting up the signs. She seemed very nice, like someone who might enjoy dancing with him in the meadow. Maybe dragons weren't so bad after all.

"I'm sorry for making you feel unwelcome. Would you like to dance?" he asked hopefully. "I'd love to!" she replied.

He grinned sheepishly and began knocking down the signs with his powerful tail.

She stepped forward and they started dancing. He felt the tickle of the grass and flowers as they pranced amongst the pansies together. The birds flying over the meadow chirped in jubilation.

The Little Dragon couldn't remember why he had felt so angry before. At first, he was nervous to share his favorite place, but he discovered that the meadow was more fun with a friend. She even taught him to control his fire so he could do useful things with it.

News about their dragon dance parties spread throughout the land and more creatures came to join in the celebration.

The Little Dragon was the happiest he'd ever been. Every night he and his new friends danced in the moonlight.

They laughed as they told stories and enjoyed freshly toasted s'mores. They lived (and danced) happily ever after.

Just like the Little Dragon, you can choose to feel your feelings and to make positive changes. Everyone has emotions and we can learn to express them in a healthy way. Sharing things that bring you joy and behaving respectfully toward others can help build friendships. Life is more fun when shared with friends.